BRAIN GAMES

This edition published in 2020 by Welbeck,
an imprint of Welbeck Non-Fiction Limited, part of Welbeck Publishing Group,
20 Mortimer Street, London, W1T 3JW

First published by Carlton Books Ltd in 1999

A CIP catalogue for this book is available from the British Library

ISBN 978-1-78739-537-4

Printed in China

Executive Editor: Tim Dedopulos
Design: Paul Messam
Production: Garry Lewis

Mensa
The High IQ Society

BRAIN GAMES

MIND-BENDING GAMES AND PUZZLES

John Bremner, Carolyn Skitt, Robert Allen

WELBECK

CONTENTS

INTRODUCTION

Word and number puzzles are always popular and here we have a selection of the finest that Mensa has to offer. You will find within this book a wide variety of types on which to test your puzzle-solving skills. In addition we have added extra elements, cards, dice, gameboards, and counters, that allow you to play a number of entertaining and challenging games. The scope is huge. We have included a puzzle-solving chase game, a word-builder, a memory game with a difference, together with a number of just-for-fun games. And just in case the anyone should think the atmosphere was getting a tad educational, we have thrown in complete instructions for playing Craps and a game called Mexican. Three of Mensa's veteran puzzle compilers, Robert Allen, Carolyn Skitt, and John Bremner have pooled their resources to come up with a pack that provides fun for the whole family and should give many hours of enjoyment.

GAME RULES

BOARD GAMES

These games involve the use of the game board.

Number nightmare

Object of the game

This game stretches your capacity to perform mathematical operations at speed. Families will find it that it gives the kids valuable practice with their maths, but adults needn't dismiss this as a children's game. You'll find it's harder than it looks. The object is to use combinations of three numbers to construct a calculation which gives you a target number.

This game uses the side of the gameboard marked with 8x8 squares.

Method of play

The numbered counters should be arranged at random with one counter covering each square of the gameboard.

One player is chosen to be the dealer. The pack of numbered cards is shuffled and each player is dealt one card face down. Play begins with the player to the left of the dealer. That person turns over his or her card and exposes the target number so that all the players can see it.

Then the players start to examine the numbers on the gameboard. The object of the game is to come up with three numbers which are adjacent horizontally, vertically or diagonally and then, by applying any mathematical processes they wish, they must reach the target number.

Example 1

The player draws the number 48. On the board he spots the numbers 4, 2 and 6 in a diagonal line. He can then score by working out that $4 \times 2 \times 6 = 48$.

Example 2

It is important to remember that ANY mathematical processes can be used. Thus if a player saw the numbers 9, 7 and 2 in a line he could take the square root of 9 which is 3, multiply it by 7 to get 21, and then multiply by 2 to get 42.

Whilst the player is attempting to find a valid calculation the other players can also look for a solution. If, after two minutes, the player whose turn it is has not come up with an answer, the first player to challenge and provide a correct answer wins that round. Play continues for an agreed number of rounds.

Puzzle piracy

This game uses the side of the game board marked with a circuit of squares. You will also need one of the dice, and each player uses four press-out counters of

the same colour as markers. The players start with all four of their counters in their home base. The object of the game is get all four counters once round the board and back into the home base.

Method of play

Each player throws the die and the one with the highest score starts the game. In the event of a tie, tied players throw again until there is a clear winner.

To get a piece out of your home base and begin the game you must throw a six. In future you must always throw a six when you want to take out another counter from your home base. Alternatively, when you throw a six you may choose to move one of your counters six squares forwards and then have another go.

Play proceeds as follows:

Each player takes a turn to throw the die. He can then move any of the pieces he has in play forward a number of squares corresponding to number shown on the die. If he lands on a square already occupied by the piece of another player then the newcomer occupies the square and the piece that was in occupation must be returned to its home base.

Puzzle squares

A number of the squares are marked as Puzzle Challenges. The pack of fifty puzzle cards should be shuffled and put on the table before play starts. If you land on a Puzzle Challenge square, the player to your left should take a card from the top of the pack and read out the puzzle. You must find the correct answer within thirty seconds (players may agree a longer time limit if children are taking part). If your answer is correct you may keep your piece on the square on which you have landed, but if you cannot answer, or your answer is wrong, you must return to the square from which you came and lose your turn. NOTE: Players may find it useful to write the puzzles down. If a player does not solve the puzzle or gives the wrong answer DO NOT read out the correct answer as this will make the game last longer. Answers are on p71-2.

The game ends when one player has taken all four of his or her pieces once round the board and back into the home base.

WORD GAMES

Here are some games you can play using the press-out letter counters and dice and the word and syllable cards.

Word wizard

This is a combination word and memory game played with the press-out cardboard dice bearing pictures of objects and the word cards. The object of the game is to use the dice and cards to discover pairs that form new words. Eg, the die with a key on one face could go with the word card 'ring' to give 'keyring'. The word on the card may go before or after the object on the die to form a pair, so you could have the word card HONEY and the die object BEE to give 'honeybee'.

Method of play

Spread the object cards out on the table face down (ie with the syllables showing). Decide which player is to start the game. The chosen player then picks one of the six dice, throws it, and turns over a card at random. It is very unlikely that in the early stages of the game pairs will be found, though it can happen. However, if the player does not find a pair, he turns the card face down again and the next player to his left takes a turn. As play continues the players will start to remember what is on the concealed faces of the cards.

When a player *does* find a pair, he removes the word card from the table and keeps it in front of him. However, this game is more difficult than a conventional memory game because even when you know what is on one of the cards, you still have to choose the right die to throw and then come up with the object that connects with the card you have chosen. As the game progresses the players are faced with the task of remembering large numbers of word cards in an effort to make new pairs. The game ends when all the word cards have been removed from play. The player with the greatest number of cards is the winner.

Bits and pieces

The letter counters are spread out face down (with number sides up). Players pick one counter each and, at an agreed signal, they turn their counter over and then have two minutes to write down as many words as possible beginning with the given letter.

Advanced Bits

Too simple? Try this variant. At each turn pick three face-down letter counters. Choose one of the letters to be the first letter of your words and then, in two minutes, come up with as many words as possible containing all three letters. For example, if you picked the letters A, T, G, you could have Astrology, Astringent, Astounding, etc.

Syllable storm

This game is played using the syllable cards and press-out letter counters. Each player is dealt five cards face up. Players then have to choose ten letter counters without looking at them. It's probably best to put the counters in a bag and let players dip in to select their counters. Each player them examines his or her hand and tries to match letters with syllables to make words. Eg, if you have the syllable ING and the letters V, A, H, then you can make HAVING. Your score for each word

is the value of the letter counters added together (the syllables have no value). At the end of each player's turn he or she must take more letter counters to replace those that have been laid down. If a player cannot make any words from his or her hand, he or she must miss a turn, but may discard five letters and replace them from the bag. The game ends when no one can make any more words. The winner is the player with the highest score when the values of all the letters used is added up.

DICE GAMES

There are many games you can play with a pair of dice, and some of the best known from around the world are here.

Craps

Craps is a classic American gambling game. It is simple to learn, uses only two dice and is fast and exciting to play. You can lose a lot of money this way if you play for cash, so play for points. Have each player start with 150 points, and the one who has the most money after a certain number of turns wins. You can bet any number of points on a turn, and the players who are not rolling the dice can choose to make a bet on the results, from the list below. If you don't make your bet or roll, you always lose the amount you bet.

The first roll in the turn is called the 'Come Out roll' and the player, known as 'the shooter', is trying to score one of the following numbers (they are known as 'point numbers'): 4, 5, 6, 8, 9, 10. If the shooter rolls a 7 or 11 the bet is paid off at even money – in other words, they gain the amount they bet. If they roll a 2, 3, or 12 then the bet is lost. If they roll a point number, then it progresses to the next stage, where the shooter has to roll the same point number again before it hits 7. Doing so successfully earns you the amount you bet, and you can choose to keep rolling, hoping to hit your point number again. When you hit 7, you lose your original bet and have to pass the dice on. You may back out before any roll without losing your bet.

Here are the major bets non-rolling players can place in Craps. If the shooter makes the point number more than once, players betting on him to pass will do too.

The Pass Bet

You bet that the shooter will throw a 7 or 11 on the come out roll or, failing that, will go on to make the point number. This pays the amount you bet.

The Don't Pass Bet

You bet against the shooter and win if craps (2, 3 or 12) is thrown on the Come Out roll or if the shooter fails to make the point.

Win Bet

You can bet on the following numbers: 4,5,6,8,9,10. It is a bet that the relevant number will be thrown BEFORE a 7. Each time the shooter throws it, you win the amount you bet.

Lose Bet

You can bet on the following numbers: 4, 5, 6, 8, 9, 10. It is a bet that a seven will be thrown BEFORE the relevant number. This pays the amount you bet.

The Come Bet

This bet is similar to the Win Bet but the number you bet on is the next number the shooter throws, not a number of your choice.

The Don't Come Bet

Again, this bet is similar to the Lose Bet, but the number you bet against is the next number the shooter throws.

Field Bet

You can bet on the outcome of the next throw. It pays the amount you bet if a 3, 4, 9,10 or 11 is thrown, and 2-1 if a 2 or 12 is thrown. You lose on 5, 6, 7 or 8.

Hardways Bet

This bet can be made on either 4,6, 8 or 10. It is a bet that the relevant number will be thrown in its double form BEFORE a 7 AND before that number is thrown in any other combination. This pays eight times your bet.

Any Seven

It pays 4 times your bet if a 7 is made in the next throw.

Any Craps

It pays 7 times your bet if a 2, 3 or 12 is made in the next throw.

Craps Two or Craps Twelve

Choose 2 or 12. This pays 30 times your bet if the number you chose is rolled on the next throw.

Craps Three or Elevens

Choose 3 or 11. This pays 15 times your bet if the number you chose is rolled on the next throw.

Horn

It pays 6 times your bet if a 2, 3, 11 or 12 is made in the next throw.

Rounders

This is a game for any number of players and uses both dice. The possible combinations of two dice are as follows: 2, 3, 4, 5, 6, 7, 8, 9, 10, 11, 12.

There are 11 rounds in this game, one for each combination. In the first round each player must try to score a total of 2. If he or she succeeds 2 points are scored. Failure gets nothing. In the second round players try to score a total of 3, etc. Thus in round 7, where the object is to score a total of 8, if a player throws a total of 8 (5+3, 4+4 or 6+2), 8 points are added to his or her score. The person with the highest score at the end of the 11th round is the winner.

Mexican

This is a game for two or more people and uses both dice. Choose a person to start the round. The idea is to throw two dice, scoring points depending on the throw, and play proceeds clockwise. When everyone has thrown the dice once, the round ends.

2 and 1is a Mexican, the highest possible roll. If you throw one of these, you get 750 points.

3 and 1is a Scum Bag. The thrower immediately loses 250 points, and has to throw again.

Any double scores 100 times the value of one die in the double, ie, double two scores 200.

Any another throw scores the highest number multiplied by 10 + the smallest number added on, ie, 5 and 4 scores 54, 6 and 1 scores 61, and so on.

In each round, the starter has the choice of one, two or three rolls to obtain the best score they can. The starter's score is the value of their last throw, so if you throw a 61 and then 63 with your first two throws then elect to take a further throw, you must count the third throw even if it is lower. Play then progresses clockwise, and every other player in the round has the choice of rolling up to as many times as the starter, ie, if the starter takes only one throw, all other players have only one throw that round. At the end of the round, the player to the starter's left is the new starter.

If a player has more than one throw available, they may choose to hold a 1 or 2 (if thrown) for subsequent throws. So, if you have two or three throws and you throw a 4 and a 1 on your first go, you may, if you wish, only pick up the 4 and throw it as your next go. You could also stick with 41 points, or roll both dice again. Holding will increase your chance of a Mexican, while also increasing your chance of a Scum Bag or a low score. If you throw a Scum Bag, you may not hold the 1.

The loser is the person who has the lowest score after every person has been the starter three times. In the event of a tie, all players with the highest score must roll one die, and the highest number is the winner.

Insert the missing numbers. In each pattern the missing number has something to do with the surrounding numbers in combination.

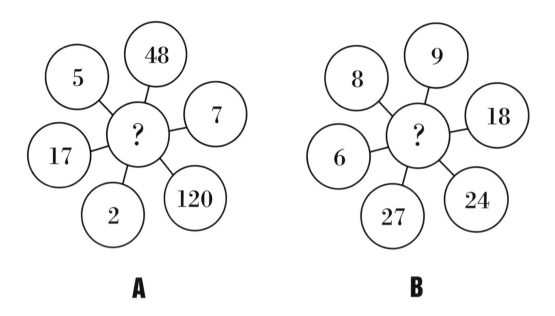

A   **B**

SEE ANSWER 21

If Picasso is worth 28 and Monet is worth 22, how much is Raphael worth?

SEE ANSWER 57

Take a five-digit number and reverse it. Subtract the original number from its reverse, and you are left with 33957.
What was the original number?

SEE ANSWER 66

PUZZLE 4

What number should replace the question mark?

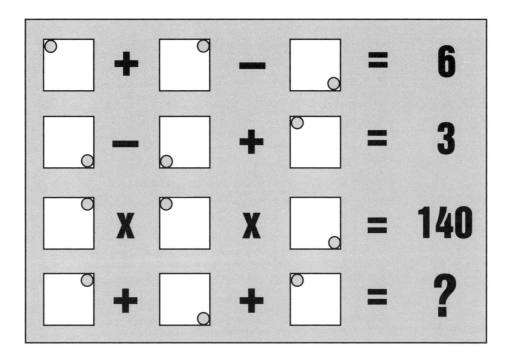

SEE ANSWER 12

Za-za is older than Fifi, but younger than Juan. Fifi is older than Jorjio and Maccio. Maccio is younger than both Carlos and Jorjio. Juan is older than both Fifi and Maccio, but younger than Carlos. Who is the oldest, and who is the youngest?

SEE ANSWER 87

{ PUZZLE 6 }

When the shaded sections of this puzzle are brought together, one of the white patches is inserted into the middle to make a magic square in which all rows, columns and long diagonals add to 49. Is it patch A, B, C or D?

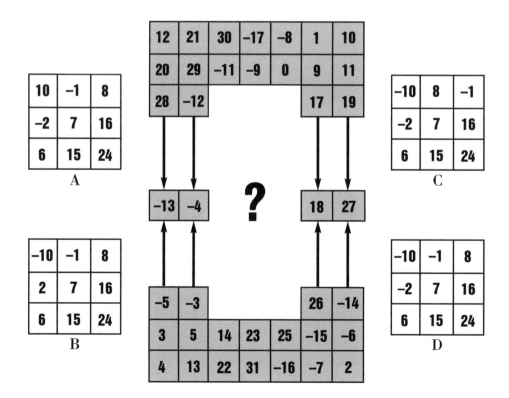

SEE ANSWER 49

A rectangular swimming pool of constant depth is twice as long as it is wide, but the owner is unhappy with the dimensions of the pool. The length is reduced by 12 units and its width increased by 10 units. When this is done, the modified pool will hold exactly the same volume of water. What were the pool's original dimensions?

SEE ANSWER 90

PUZZLE 8

Each shape is made up of two items, and each same shape has the same value, whether in the foreground or background. What number should replace the question mark?

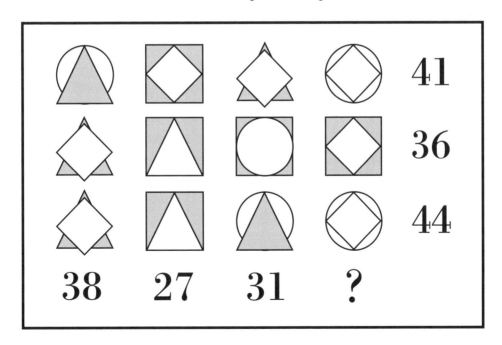

SEE ANSWER 23

What is the area of the shaded path, if the path is one unit wide?

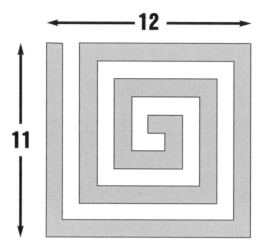

SEE ANSWER 52

PUZZLE 10

The panel below, when complete, contains the binary numbers from 1 to 25. Does binary patch A, B, C or D complete the panel?

1	1	0	1	1	1	0	0	1	0	1
1	1	0	1	1	1	1	0	0	0	1
0	0	1	1	0	1	0	1	0	1	1
1	1	0						1	1	1
0	1	1		?				0	0	1
0	0	0						0	1	0
0	1	1	1	0	1	0	0	1	0	1
0	1	1	0	1	1	0	1	0	1	1
1	1	1	0	0	0	1	1	0	0	1

1	0	1	1	1
1	1	1	1	0
1	1	1	0	0

A

0	1	1	0	1
1	1	1	0	0
0	1	0	0	1

B

1	1	0	1	1
1	1	0	1	1
0	0	1	0	1

C

0	1	1	0	1
1	1	1	0	0
1	1	0	0	1

D

SEE ANSWER 82

Which letters, based on the alphanumeric system, should go into the blank boxes?

6	1	7	3
1	3	5	4
7	7	0	9

A H B

5	1	3	9
2	8	6	4
8	6	2	6

F B C

2	2	9	2
4	3	0	9
7	1	7	8

SEE ANSWER 15

What number, when you multiply it by 5 and add 6, then multiply that result by 4 and add 9, gives you a number that, when you multiply it by 5 and subtract 165, gives you a number that, when you knock off the last 2 digits, brings you back to your original number?

SEE ANSWER 5

What number should replace the question mark?

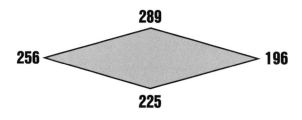

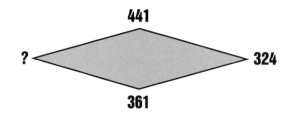

SEE ANSWER 34

If each large ball weighs one and a third times the weight of each little ball, what is the minimum number of balls that need to be added to the right-hand side to make the scales balance?

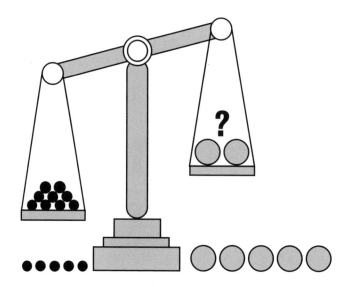

SEE ANSWER 74

PUZZLE 15

Present at Juan's birthday party were a father-in-law, a
mother-in-law, a daughter-in-law, two sons, two daughters, two
sisters and a brother, four children, three grandchildren, two
fathers, two mothers, a grandfather, and a grandmother.
However, family relationships can be complicated.
One man's brother can, of course, be another man's
brother-in-law, and at the same time, someone's son.
With that in mind, what is the smallest number of people
needed at the party for the above relationships to exist?

SEE ANSWER 4

PUZZLE 16

How many rosettes are missing from the blank circle?

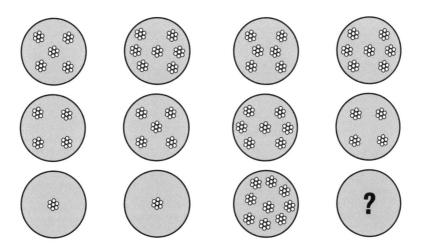

SEE ANSWER 62

Forty people took part in a freestyle race. Twenty people ran. Ten people dashed. Five people bolted and sprinted. Three people bolted, dashed, ran and sprinted. Two people ran, bolted, and sprinted. Five people ran and sprinted. Two people dashed, ran, and sprinted. How many people neither dashed, ran, bolted, nor sprinted?

SEE ANSWER 32

PUZZLE 18

What value needs to go into the upper box to bring this system into balance? Note: The beam is broken down into equal parts and the value of each box is taken from its midpoint.

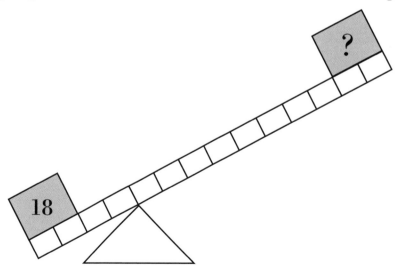

SEE ANSWER 94

PUZZLE 19

Find a route from the top of this puzzle to the bottom that arrives at the total 353, always going down and to an adjoining hexagon.

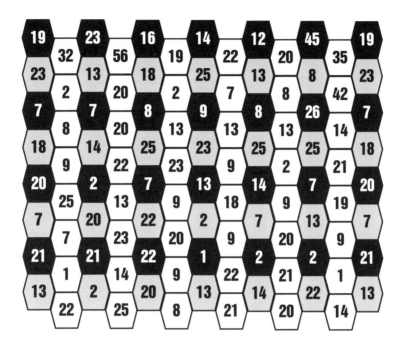

SEE ANSWER 25

PUZZLE 20

Using only the numbers already used, complete this puzzle to make all the rows, columns, and long diagonals add to 27.

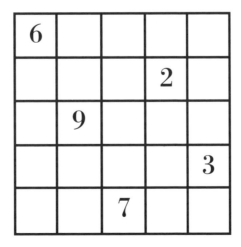

SEE ANSWER 91

Insert the supplied rows of numbers into the appropriate places in the grid to make all rows, columns and long diagonals add to 17.
Example: (C) goes into the location (a).

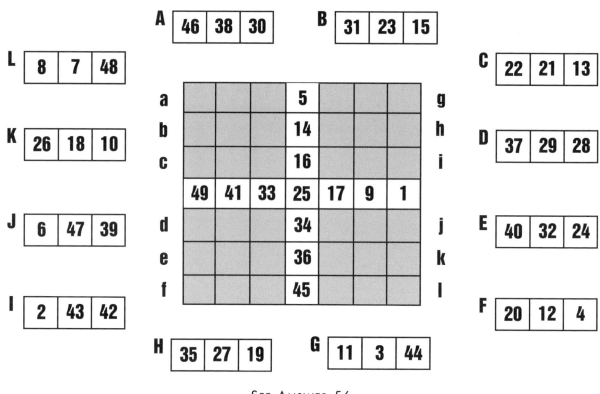

SEE ANSWER 56

PUZZLE 22

At 3pm one day, a flagpole and a measuring pole cast shadows as shown. What length is the flagpole?

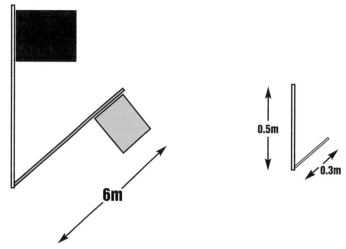

SEE ANSWER 10

Use logic to discover which shape has the greatest perimeter.

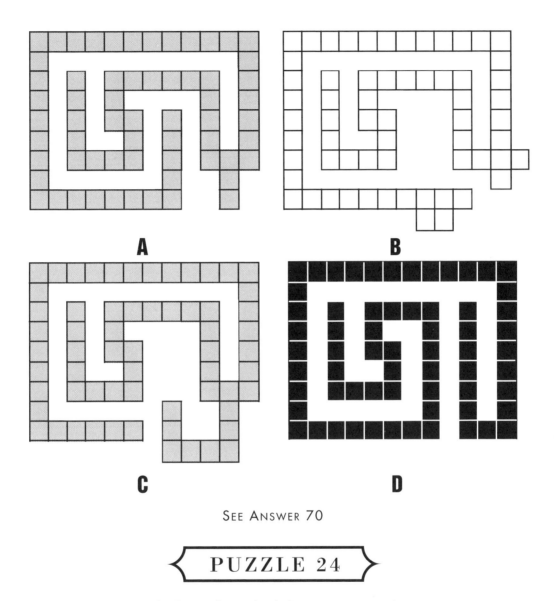

SEE ANSWER 70

PUZZLE 24

Crack the code to find the missing number.

A	B	C	D	E	F	G	H	I	J
9	3	8	7	8	9	2	8	5	7
1	2	1	5	?	7	1	0	1	2
K	L	M	N	O	P	Q	R	S	T

What number should replace the question mark?

6 8 4 8 7 9 6 ?

SEE ANSWER 41

PUZZLE 26

Which number replaces the question mark?
What is the value of each animal?

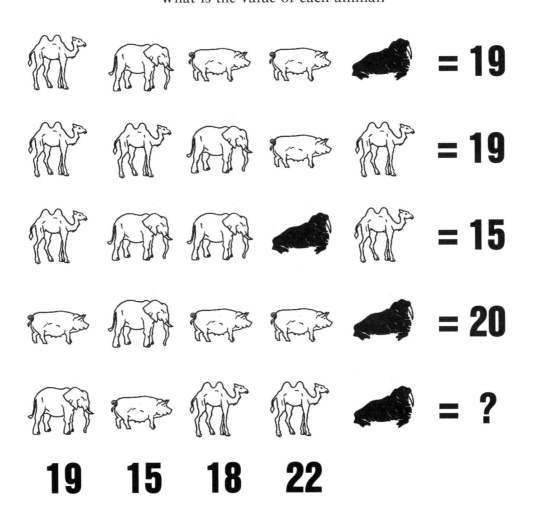

19   15   18   22

SEE ANSWER 31

What number should replace the question mark?

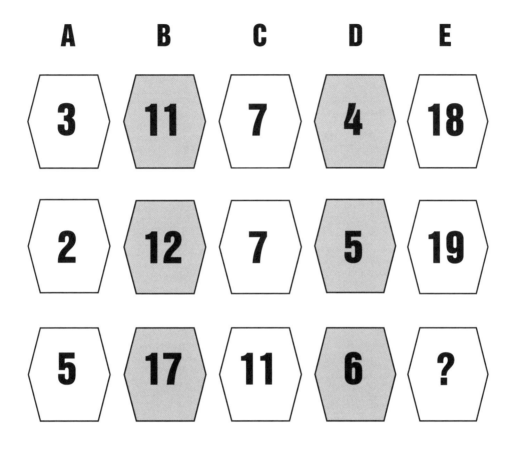

SEE ANSWER 17

PUZZLE 28

If it takes 5 men to dig 5 holes in 5 hours, how many men does it take to dig 100 holes in 100 hours?

SEE ANSWER 96

Put the right number in the blank star.

SEE ANSWER 46

PUZZLE 30

If you buy 9 barrels of beer for 25 Credits each, but you are given a 25% discount on the last 4 barrels, and you are given in change 3 times the cost of all the barrels less half the value that your discount would be if your discount were 25% more for the last 2 barrels than the discount you were actually given, what was the total cost of the barrels ?

SEE ANSWER 101

Can you work out what letter needs to be inserted in the middle to
form four dances by combining opposite segments?

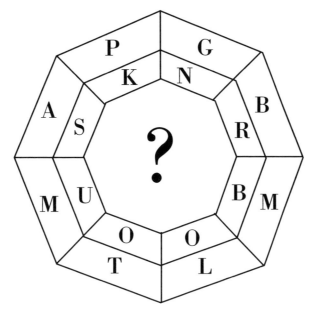

See Answer 40

Move from square to touching square – including diagonals – to
discover the name of a city.

P	H	N	G
C	E	A	G
P	O	E	N

See Answer 54

At an exhibition there are 207 Calvin Klein creations, 512 outfits by Vivienne Westwood and 100 Jasper Conran outfits. How many items by Giorgio Armani are there at the exhibition?

SEE ANSWER 75

PUZZLE 34

The names of the following ten chefs can be found in this grid on either vertical, horizontal or diagonal lines. Can you find them?

Raymond Blanc

Paul Bocuse

Robert Carrier

Keith Floyd

Rosamund Grant

Ken Hom

Bruno Loubet

Gary Rhodes

Albert Roux

Anthony Tobin

T	N	A	R	G	D	N	U	M	A	S	O	R
B	Y	N	L	K	L	Q	O	X	C	B	O	A
Q	W	T	F	Z	P	H	K	U	J	B	G	Y
Y	G	H	V	S	N	X	E	O	R	C	M
D	V	O	W	E	M	D	I	R	S	U	K	O
J	K	N	K	D	B	P	T	T	U	N	O	N
P	M	Y	S	O	S	C	H	R	C	O	P	D
P	F	T	Y	H	A	Y	F	E	O	L	J	B
Z	W	O	U	R	Z	G	L	B	B	O	C	L
F	C	B	R	Y	Q	K	O	L	L	U	F	A
Y	V	I	D	R	J	F	Y	A	U	B	R	N
W	E	N	V	A	Y	Q	D	P	A	E	W	C
R	G	K	P	G	R	Z	B	Y	P	T	P	Q

SEE ANSWER 2

By taking a segment and finding its pair the names of four books
from the Old Testament can be made. What are they?

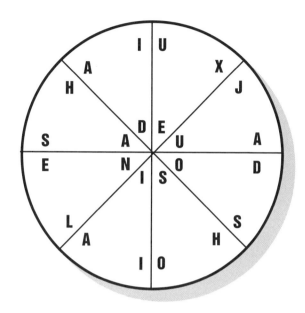

SEE ANSWER 84

In the china department of a large store there are 90 items of Wedgewood, 120 items of Royal Doulton and 140 items of Royal Worcester. How many items of Spode are there?

SEE ANSWER 42

Rearrange each of the following groups of letters to form a place in the United States. Which is the odd one out?

AILFORD

ALEEWARD

ORKNYBOL

OZARNIA

SEE ANSWER 73

PUZZLE 38

If the code for Monica Seles is **GIHCWU MYFYM** who are these other famous tennis stars?

(i)   **JUN WUMB**

(ii)   **MNYZZC ALUZ**

(iii)   **UHXLY UAUMMC**

(iv)   **GULNCHU HUPLUNCFIPU**

(v)   **WIHWBCNU GULNCHYT**

SEE ANSWER 11

In a car race six cars are lined up behind each other. No. 12 is two places in front of No. 3 who is two places in front of No. 21. No. 7 is behind both No. 11 and No. 3 but in front of No. 21. No. 8 is in front of No. 21 but behind No. 11. What is the finishing order of the cars if car No. 21 moves forward two positions, car No. 8 moves back 3 places, car No. 3 moves forward two places, car No. 11 moves back two places and car No. 12 moves forward one place?

SEE ANSWER 64

{ PUZZLE 40 }

What is the next letter in this sequence?

C H L O ?

SEE ANSWER 26

Adam drinks Advocaat and he drives a Datsun. He has a collection of albums by Annie Lennox. Does Adam fly with Virgin or Monarch airline?

SEE ANSWER 78

Rearrange these four American states in the grid provided so that a European currency can be read down the shaded boxes:

Arkansas, Maryland, Illinois and Michigan.

What is the currency?

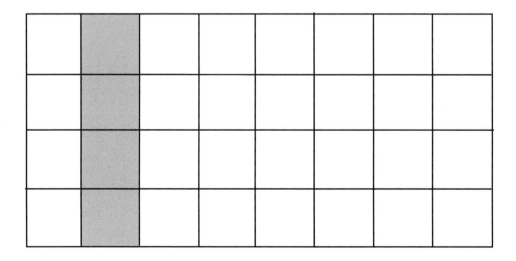

SEE ANSWER 51

Complete the square with the letters of P A R I S. When completed
no row, column or diagonal line will contain the same letter more
than once. One horizontal line will spell the word correctly.
What letter should replace the question mark?

P	A	R		
			?	
		S	P	

SEE ANSWER 81

Collect one letter from each segment to give the name of an
American state. What is it?

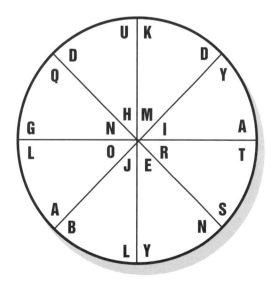

SEE ANSWER 8

PUZZLE 45

What letter is missing from the end turret?
Clue: Actors

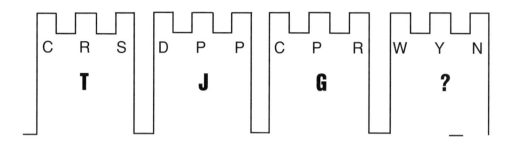

C	R	S	D	P	P	C	P	R	W	Y	N
T			**J**			**G**			**?**		

SEE ANSWER 93

PUZZLE 46

Two sides of this pyramid can be seen, but the other two are obscured. Two eight-letter country names are written round the pyramid. What are they?

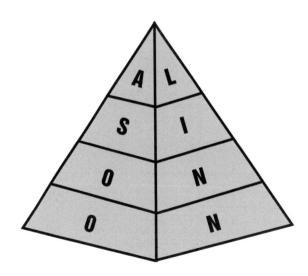

SEE ANSWER 37

A knight, which moves either one square horizontally and two vertically or two horizontally and one vertically, is positioned on this unusual chess board on position A1. Move to each square once in the correct sequence to find the names of four famous scientists.

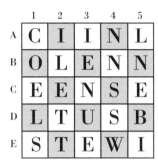

SEE ANSWER 99

PUZZLE 48

This is an unusual maze. Find four separate routes through the maze without any route crossing another, although they may share the same path. On each route collect 7 letters only to give you the names of four books in the Old Testament.

FINISH

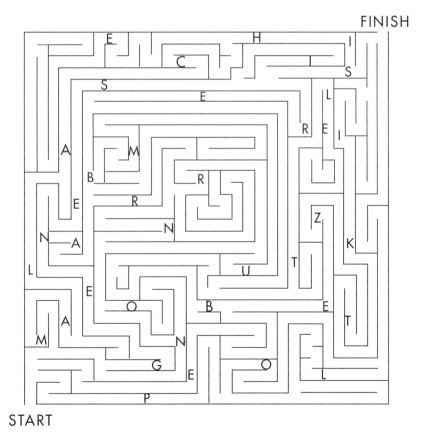

START

SEE ANSWER 68

In a horse race Sawgrass came second and Sea Dancer came fourth.

Where did Sky Trap and Noble Romance finish?

SEE ANSWER 97

Some letters have been omitted from this alphabet.
Use the missing letters to form the name of a car manufacturer.

W K C Y D Z I B H
G X P F
M O J S V Q

SEE ANSWER 27

PUZZLE 51

If the name WOODROW WILSON is

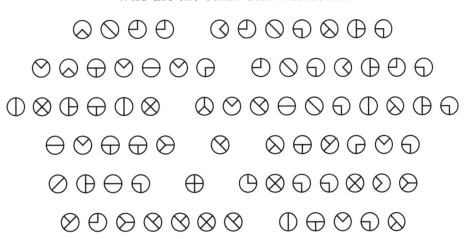

Who are the other U.S. Presidents?

See Answer 19

PUZZLE 52

Looking at one side of a bus with two rows of single
seats you can see four seats upstairs and four downstairs.
Mrs Davis is sitting two seats behind Mr Evans.
Mrs Graves is sitting above Mrs Bates
and Mr Adams is sitting above Mr Connors.
Mr Evans sits above Mrs Harris at the front of the bus.
Mr Connors is sitting three seats behind Mrs Harris.
Mrs Davis sits on the top deck and Mr Francis
sits behind Mrs Bates on the lower deck.
Who is sitting where?

See Answer 79

Laura wears Chanel clothes and her perfume is Oscar de la Renta. Her favourite sculptor is Jules Dalou and she likes Royal Worcester for her dinner service. Is Laura's favourite tennis player Martina Navratilova or Steffi Graf?

SEE ANSWER 35

PUZZLE 54

Move from square to touching square – including diagonals – to discover the name of a car.

O	R	L	K
B	A	G	N
M	H	I	I

SEE ANSWER 104

The names of the following ten perfumes can be found in this grid on vertical, horizontal and diagonal lines. Can you find them?

Amarige

Anais Anais

Coco

Dune

Miss Dior

Obsession

Paris

Safari

Samsara

Spellbound

S	I	A	N	A	S	I	A	N	A
A	P	D	G	H	F	P	J	C	R
F	C	E	G	I	R	A	M	A	A
A	F	H	L	D	J	R	K	F	S
R	Y	Q	U	L	Z	I	Z	R	M
I	R	N	Z	X	B	S	F	X	A
Q	E	V	K	W	O	O	Y	J	S
B	H	K	V	D	W	C	U	G	I
O	B	S	E	S	S	I	O	N	G
R	O	I	D	S	S	I	M	C	D

SEE ANSWER 3

**If there have been
13 Malaysia Airline flights,
22 Virgin Atlantic flights and
16 Pan Am flights this week,
how many Cathay Pacific
flights have there been?**

SEE ANSWER 59

PUZZLE 57

The letters surrounding each triangle are the consonants of a famous sports person's name. The letters inside the triangle have a connection with each person. What letter should replace the question mark in the fourth triangle?

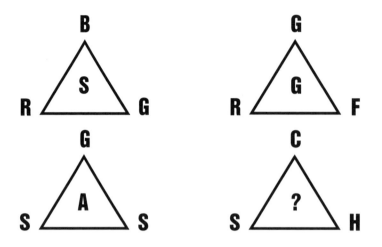

SEE ANSWER 86

PUZZLE 58

If the country UNITED STATES is

Which are these states?

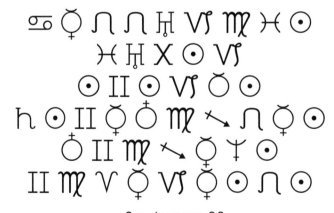

SEE ANSWER 33

PUZZLE 59

Turn the dials on this diagram to give 8 forenames and 8 surnames of famous actresses. Then match them up to give their full names. Who are they? (A score above 5 is very good!)

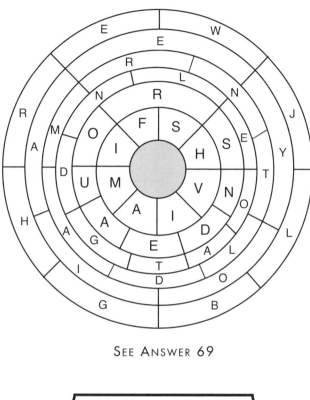

SEE ANSWER 69

PUZZLE 60

The names of the following ten film stars can be found in this grid on vertical, horizontal and diagonal lines. Can you find them?

John Cleese

Tom Cruise

Mel Gibson

Hugh Grant

Tom Hanks

Val Kilmer

Bruce Lee

Al Pacino

Sean Penn

Brad Pitt

W	Z	Q	E	P	R	V	H	E	F	M
T	O	U	S	Y	J	A	H	E	E	Z
T	N	S	I	G	K	L	U	L	S	W
I	I	E	U	F	H	K	G	E	E	P
P	C	A	R	H	X	I	H	C	E	H
D	A	N	C	H	B	L	G	U	L	J
A	P	P	M	S	Q	M	R	R	C	R
R	L	E	O	J	R	E	A	B	N	G
B	A	N	T	T	Z	R	N	P	H	Y
S	K	N	A	H	M	O	T	W	O	S
Y	R	B	X	F	Q	J	X	N	J	S

SEE ANSWER 1

PUZZLE 61

How far should it be to Las Vegas on this strange signpost?

SEE ANSWER 38

PUZZLE 62

What letter has been missed from the last box?

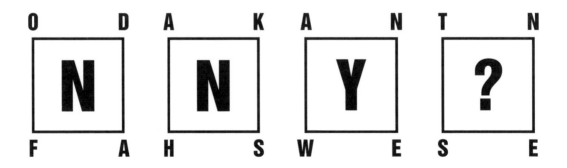

SEE ANSWER 100

40

By taking a segment and finding its pair, four
film stars can be found. Who are they?

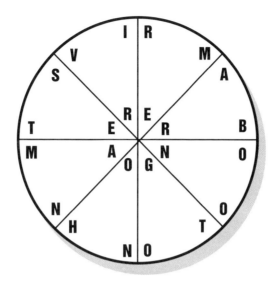

SEE ANSWER 55

{ PUZZLE 64 }

Starting from any square on the top row, you can accumulate points
by stepping down diagonally to another, adjoining square, and
adding that to your total. You may not land on a square containing
the number one, or on any square horizontally adjacent to a square
with a one, but you may start from such a square.
You may not travel up or sideways. By continuing this process until
you reach a square on the bottom row, what is the maximum
number of points it is possible to accumulate?

9	4	5	3	6	1	8	2
8	1	2	2	3	2	5	1
6	9	9	1	2	4	3	5
4	8	1	3	5	2	6	1
1	4	3	7	6	3	1	4
9	2	4	8	6	4	5	3
4	2	9	4	8	6	7	1
2	8	1	6	5	9	0	1

SEE ANSWER 13

PUZZLE 65

When a ball is dropped from a height of 9 m, it bounces back two-thirds of the way. Assuming that the ball comes to rest after making a bounce which takes it less than 2 mm high, how many times does it bounce?

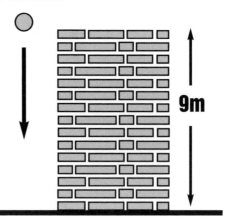

9m

SEE ANSWER 88

PUZZLE 66

The planet Pento is inhabited by a race of highly intelligent one-toed quadrupeds with elephant-like trunks. So with four toes and a trunk, they have adopted the five base for their number system. With that in mind, convert the Pento number 1234 into its decimal equivalent.

SEE ANSWER 39

Which number should replace the question mark?

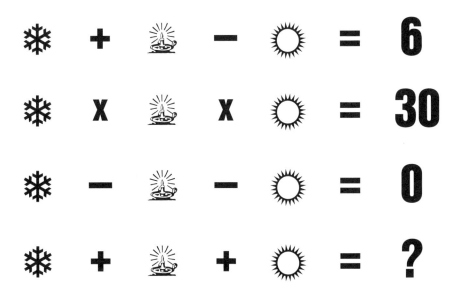

SEE ANSWER 76

PUZZLE 68

These systems are in balance. What weight is required in
the right hand box to balance the load ?

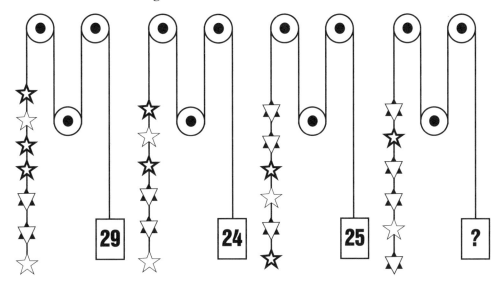

SEE ANSWER 6

Each same shape has the same value. What number should
replace the question mark

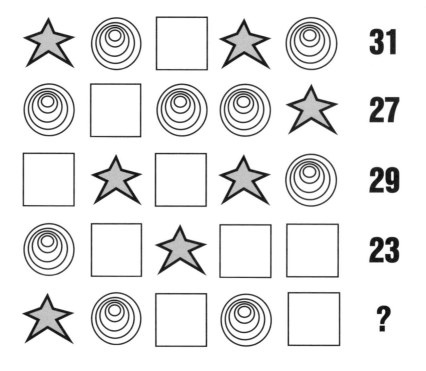

SEE ANSWER 53

Find the missing number.

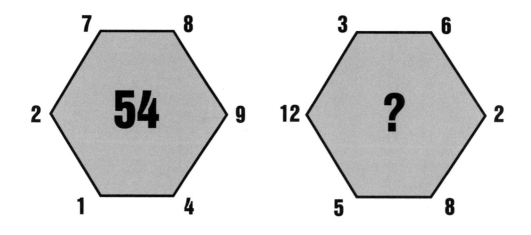

SEE ANSWER 36

What three-digit number should replace the question mark?

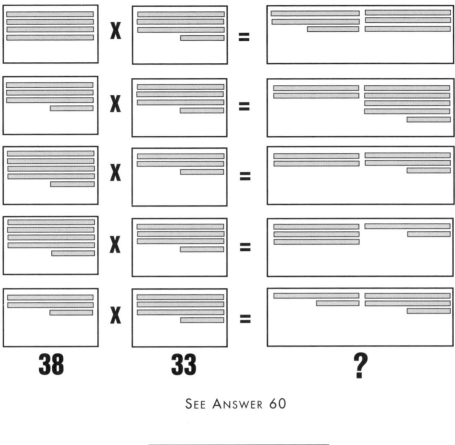

38   **33**   **?**

SEE ANSWER 60

This clock has been designed for a planet that rotates on its axis once every 16 hours. There are 64 minutes to every hour, and 64 seconds to the minute. At the moment, the time on the clock reads a quarter to eight. What time, to the nearest second, will the clock say the time after the next time the hands appear to meet?

SEE ANSWER 105

The three balls at the top of each hexagon should contain numbers that, when added together and subtracted from the total of the numbers in the three balls at the bottom of each hexagon, equal the number inside each relevant hexagon. Insert the missing numbers.

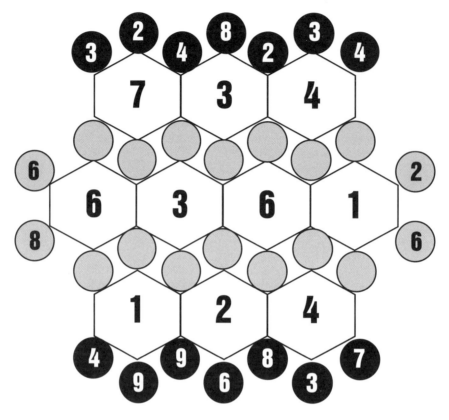

SEE ANSWER 18

What number, when added to a number 10 times as big, gives a number that, when its right-hand digit is multiplied by four and added to the result of the above, gives 1000?

SEE ANSWER 103

A large sheet of paper is 0.1 mm thick. A man amuses
himself by tearing it in half and putting both pieces together,
and then tearing those into four sheets, and repeating the
process until he has done it twenty-five times.
How high is the stack of paper now?

a) As thick as a book   b) As high as a man   c) As high as a house
d) As high as a mountain

SEE ANSWER 71

This is a time puzzle. Which symbol is missing ?
Is it A, B, C, D, E or F?

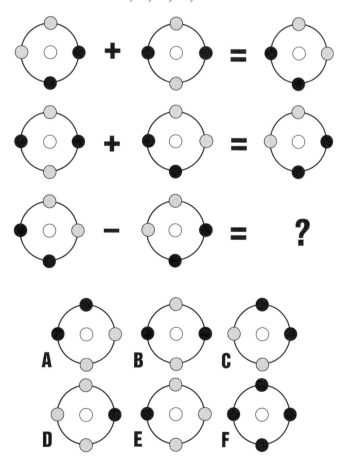

SEE ANSWER 14

Which number should replace the question mark?

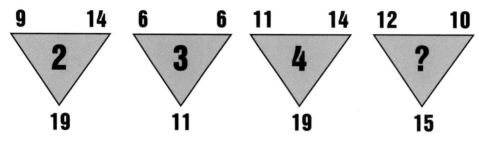

SEE ANSWER 63

PUZZLE 78

Insert in the boxes at the corner of each shaded number-square, the digits which are multiplied together to give the numbers in the shaded boxes. For example, in the bottom left corner, 144 is derived from 3 x 6 x 8 (and another multiplier – here 1), but you also have to consider how this helps to make solutions for the surrounding numbers… and so on.

3		5		4		4		3		3
	90		120		64		144		54	
2										1
	48		96		16		72		36	
1										2
	160		80		20		150		30	
4										1
	180		10		40		100		15	
9										3
	27		8		32		12		81	
3										9
	24		28		84		45		135	
8										1
	144		42		63		225		25	
3		6		1		3		5		1

SEE ANSWER 44

What number should replace the question mark?

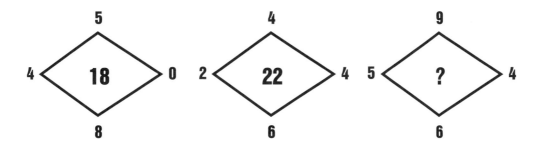

SEE ANSWER 89

Each like symbol has the same value. Supply the missing total.

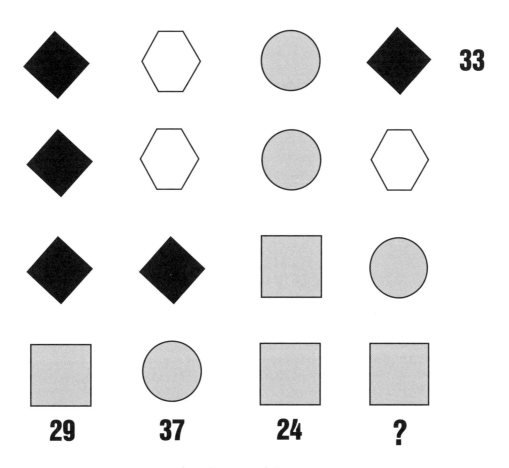

SEE ANSWER 24

What time will it be, to the nearest second, when the hands of this clock next appear to meet?

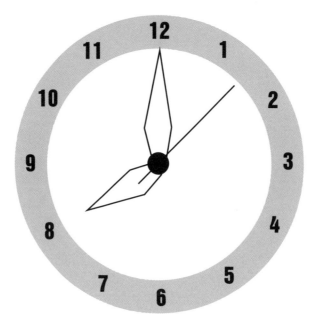

SEE ANSWER 92

PUZZLE 82

What number should replace the question mark?

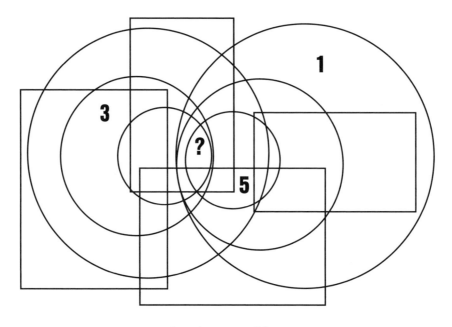

SEE ANSWER 50

Insert the missing numbers in the blank hexagons.

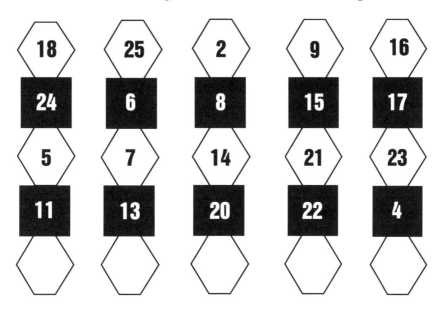

SEE ANSWER 98

PUZZLE 84

What number should replace the question mark?

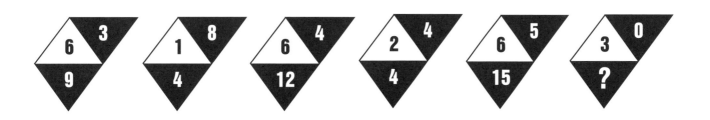

SEE ANSWER 7

What number should replace the question mark?

9	7	2	5	7	4	3	2	5	1
									4
9	4	5	2	7	5	2	7		5
3							9		9
6		?	2	6	5	1	8		8
2									1
8	3	5	2	7	4	3	3	6	5

SEE ANSWER 65

Black counters are nominally worth 4.
White counters are nominally worth 3.
Being on a diagonal trebles a counter's value.
Being on the innermost box doubles a counter's value.
Being on the outermost box halves a counter's value.
The rules work in combination.
What is the total value of all the counters on the board?

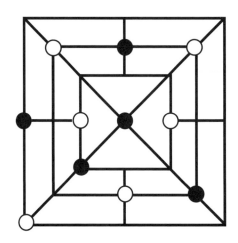

SEE ANSWER 47

What number continues the sequence?

| 15 | 20 | 20 | 6 | 6 | ? |

SEE ANSWER 28

PUZZLE 88

I have a deck of cards from which some are missing. If I deal them equally between nine people, I have two cards to spare. If I deal them equally between four people, I have three cards to spare. If I deal them between seven people, I have five cards to spare. There are normally 52 cards in the deck.

How many are missing?

SEE ANSWER 83

Each same symbol has the same value. What number should replace the question mark?

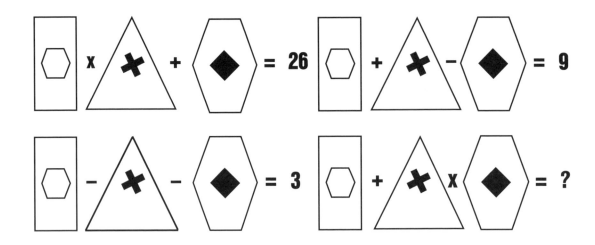

SEE ANSWER 16

PUZZLE 90

What number should replace the question mark?

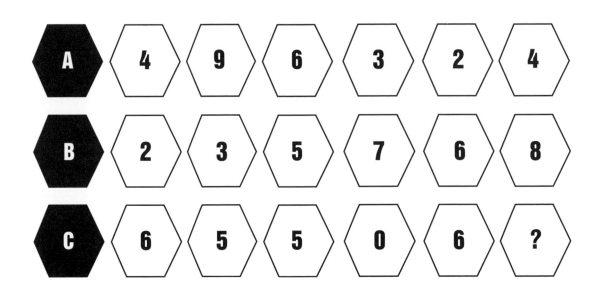

SEE ANSWER 58

What number should replace the question mark in the blank square?

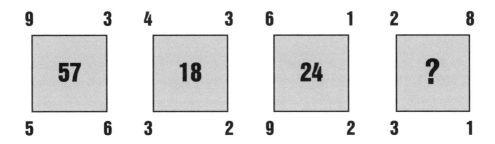

SEE ANSWER 95

Insert the central numbers.

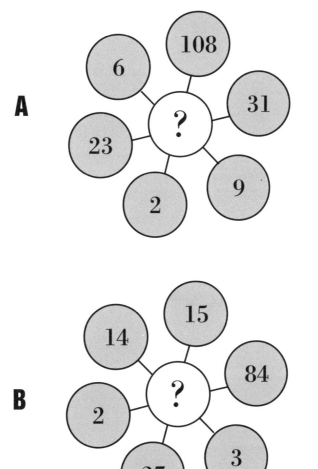

SEE ANSWER 30

Along a street there are 7 Ford cars, 9 Toyota cars and 13 Alfa Romeo cars.

How many Mazda cars are there?

SEE ANSWER 106

The vowels have been missed out of the following groups of letters. Replace the vowels and rearrange each group to form the name of a film star. Who are the four stars?

STND FFMHN
VST RNMT
TRCPK YZSW
LMN FFGTHRS

SEE ANSWER 9

The names of three lakes have been merged together here.
Which are they?

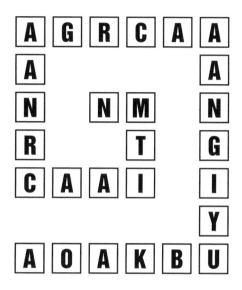

SEE ANSWER 45

PUZZLE 96

If the term ANCIENT GODS is

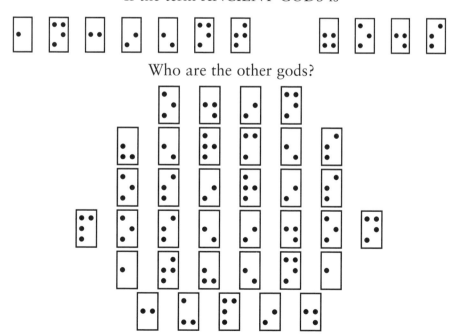

Who are the other gods?

SEE ANSWER 67

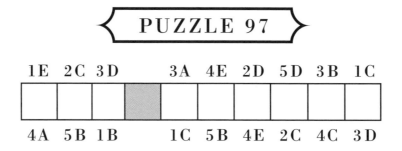

PUZZLE 97

1E	2C	3D		3A	4E	2D	5D	3B	1C
4A	5B	1B		1C	5B	4E	2C	4C	3D

The word frame above, when filled with the correct letters, will give the name of a film star. The letters are arranged in the coded square below. There are two possible alternatives to fill each square of the word frame, one correct, the other incorrect. Who is the film star?

	A	**B**	**C**	**D**	**E**
1	A	L	R	F	M
2	Q	J	E	H	C
3	G	Y	P	N	W
4	D	Z	O	K	B
5	T	I	V	S	X

SEE ANSWER 102

PUZZLE 98

What letters are missing from this sequence?

A S ? ? G H J

SEE ANSWER 20

Six people go into a store through the underground car park going to floors 1, 2, 3, 4, 5 and 6. Each person goes to a different floor in the same elevator, which goes up stopping at each floor. Eddie's ride is the longest. Angie gets out before Frankie but after Debbie. Charlie gets out first. Barbie leaves before Debbie, who leaves at the third floor.

At what floor does each person leave?

SEE ANSWER 80

Jean is a relation of the scientist Jenner. Jean was born in Denver but now lives in Seattle.

Is Jean is a bigger fan of tennis player Sampras or McEnroe?

SEE ANSWER 72

PUZZLE 101

The people listed below were told that they could win a car if they could arrange their names in the grid below to give the car's manufacturer down the shaded column. What car did they get? Their names were:

BRUCE DIANA SARAH BRIAN BILLY MARIE

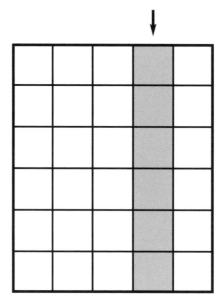

SEE ANSWER 29

PUZZLE 102

Two sides of this pyramid can be seen, but the other two are obscured. Two eight-letter American states are written around the pyramid. What are they?

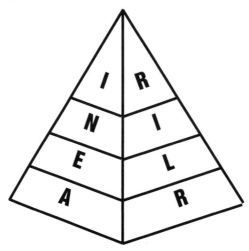

SEE ANSWER 77

A knight, which moves either one square horizontally and two vertically or two horizontally and one vertically, starts at the shaded square of this chess board visiting each square without returning to the same square twice. Find the route which spells out six famous movie stars.

O	T	E	S	I	O	T	I
M	O	P	S	L	B	G	R
E	O	G	N	D	N	G	O
N	E	B	O	R	A	I	O
H	V	E	J	D	L	M	T
S	R	A	E	F	D	R	N
E	W	B	U	A	I	R	C
O	I	M	N	E	R	E	T

SEE ANSWER 48

This list of English monarchs shows the fictitious number of years they reigned. Can you think of a monarch who would have reigned for less than a year?

Mary	**17**
James	**12**
George	**10**
Charles	**7**
William	**3**

SEE ANSWER 22

In a large raffle
Ian had ticket number one,
Vivian had number twelve
and David had number 1006.

Who of the following had ticket
numbers 500, 60, 1000 and 151
from Axel, Charlie,
Brenda and Norman?

SEE ANSWER 61

PUZZLE 106

Some letters are missing from this alphabet. Rearrange the missing letters to form the name of a European city.

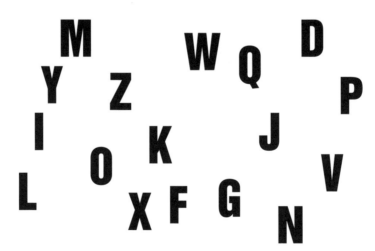

SEE ANSWER 43

1

W	Z	Q	E	P	R	V	H	E	F	M
T	O	U	S	Y	J	A	H	E	E	Z
T	N	S	I	G	K	L	U	L	S	W
I	I	E	U	F	H	K	G	E	E	P
P	C	A	R	H	X	I	H	C	E	H
D	A	N	C	H	B	L	G	U	L	J
A	P	P	M	S	Q	M	R	R	C	R
R	L	E	O	J	R	E	A	B	N	G
B	A	N	T	T	Z	R	N	P	H	Y
S	K	N	A	H	M	O	T	W	O	S
Y	R	B	X	F	Q	J	X	N	J	S

2

T	N	A	R	G	D	N	U	M	A	S	O	R
B	Y	N	L	K	L	Q	O	X	C	B	O	A
Q	W	T	F	Z	P	H	K	U	J	B	G	Y
Y	G	H	V	S	N	X	E	O	R	C	M	
D	V	O	W	E	M	D	I	R	S	U	K	O
J	K	N	K	D	B	P	T	T	U	N	O	N
P	M	Y	S	O	S	C	H	R	C	O	P	D
P	F	T	Y	H	A	Y	F	E	O	L	J	B
Z	W	O	U	R	Z	G	L	B	B	O	C	L
F	C	B	R	Y	Q	K	O	L	L	U	F	A
Y	V	I	D	R	J	F	Y	A	U	B	R	N
W	E	N	V	A	Y	Q	D	P	A	E	W	C
R	G	K	P	G	R	Z	B	Y	P	T	P	Q

3

S	I	A	N	A	S	I	A	N	A
A	P	D	G	H	F	P	J	C	R
F	C	E	G	I	R	A	M	A	A
A	F	H	L	D	J	R	K	F	S
R	Y	Q	U	L	Z	I	Z	R	M
I	R	N	Z	X	B	S	F	X	A
Q	E	V	K	W	O	O	Y	J	S
B	H	K	V	D	W	C	U	G	I
O	B	S	E	S	S	I	O	N	G
R	O	I	D	S	S	I	M	C	D

4   7 people.

5   Any number. This amazing formula will always end up with the number you first thought of, with 00 at the end.

6   24. The pieces have the following values:

☆ = 5

▽ = 4

☆ = 3

7   0. The top two numbers are multiplied in shapes 1, 3 and 5. The answers are put as single-digit numbers in the top triangles of shapes 2, 4 and 6. In all the shapes the top two numbers are multiplied, then halved, 3 x 0 = 0.

8   Maryland.

9   Dustin Hoffman
Steve Martin
Patrick Swayze
Melanie Griffiths

10   10 m. The ratio of the flagpole to its shadow is the same as the ratio of the measuring stick to its shadow.

11   (The alphabet is 6 letters out of phase)
  i)   Pat Cash
  ii)   Steffi Graf
  iii) Andre Agassi
  iv)   Martina Navratilova
  v)   Conchita Martinez

12   16.

 = 4   = 5

 = 6   = 7

13   46 points, taking this route:

9	4	5	3	6	1	8	2
8	1	2	2	3	2	5	1
6	9	9	1	2	4	3	5
4	8	1	3	5	2	6	1
1	4	3	7	6	3	1	4
9	2	4	8	6	4	5	3
4	2	9	4	8	6	7	1
2	8	1	6	5	9	0	1

14   B. The shaded spots represent the hands of a clock. 3:00 – 9:00 = 6:00.

15   E, G, G. These represent the numbers 577, which are added to the sum of the previous top and middle line, to get the bottom line.

16   22.
Rectangle = 8
Triangle = 3
Hexagon = 2

17   28. Each row is a sequence of A + D = C, D + C = B and B + C = E.

18

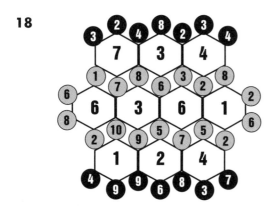

19   i)   Bill Clinton
ii)   Abraham Lincoln
iii) George Washington
iv)   Harry S. Truman
v)   John F. Kennedy
vi)   Ulysses Grant

20   D and F. On a Qwerty keyboard, these are the first letters, reading from the left, of the middle row.

21   A. 24. Opposite numbers are divided or added to give 24.
B. 3. Opposite numbers are multiplied or divided by 3.

22   Queen Anne. The number of spaces in the alphabet between the second and third letters of each person's name.

23   25.
Circle = 4
Triangle = 8
Diamond = 5
Square = 2
The values are added when the shapes are combined.

24   32.
Diamond = 7
Circle = 4
Hexagon = 13
Square = 8

25   Follow this route.

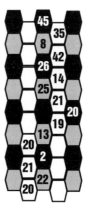

26 Q. The alphabet is moved five letters, then four, then three, etc.

27 Renault.

28 19. They denote the alphanumeric positions of numbers from 1 to 6. The first letter of six is "s", the 19th letter of the alphabet.

29 Lancia.

B	I	L	L	Y
B	R	I	A	N
D	I	A	N	A
B	R	U	C	E
M	A	R	I	E
S	A	R	A	H

30 A. 54, B. 42. Opposite numbers are multiplied, divided, or added to get the numbers in the middle.

31 18.
Elephant = 2
Walrus = 3
Camel = 4
Pig = 5

32 10 people.

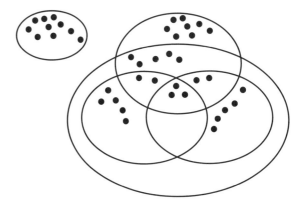

33 i)   Minnesota
ii)   Texas
iii) Alaska
iv) California
v)   Florida
vi) Louisiana

34 400. The numbers are the squares of 14 to 21 inclusive.

35 Martina Navratilova. The last letters placed together give the name Laura.

36 78. Multiply opposite numbers and add the results to get the numbers in the middle. Thus 24 + 24 + 30 = 78.

37 Malaysia and Hong Kong.

38 340. Each vowel is given a value of 30 and each consonant is given a value of 50. These are added together in each city name to give the distance.

39 194. $(1 \times 5^3) + (2 \times 5^2) + (3 \times 5^1) + (4 \times 5^0)$.

40 A. Tango
Polka
Rumba
Samba

41 3. There are two sequences in the series: 6 x 8 = 48, and 7 x 9 = 63.

42 50. The number of letters in each name, multiplied by 10, gives the amount.

43 Bucharest.

44

3		5		4		4		3		3
	90		120		64		144		54	
2		3		2		2		6		1
	48		96		16		72		36	
1		8		2		2		3		2
	160		80		20		150		30	
4		5		1		5		5		1
	180		10		40		100		15	
9		1		2		4		1		3
	27		8		32		12		81	
3		1		4		1		3		9
	24		28		84		45		135	
8		1		7		3		5		1
	144		42		63		225		25	
3		6		1		3		5		1

45 Nicaragua
Maracaibo
Tanganyka

46 6. Add the value of the top two stars of each column to value of the middle two stars to get the value of the bottom two stars.

47 103.5

48 The stars are: Tom Cruise, Mel Gibson, Robert De Niro, Steve Martin, Whoopi Goldberg, and Jane Fonda.

O 45	T 32	E 11	S 16	I 47	O 30	T 1	I 14
M 10	O 17	P 46	S 31	L 12	B 15	G 48	R 29
E 33	O 44	G 55	N 58	D 51	N 62	G 13	O 2
N 18	E 9	B 52	O 61	R 54	A 57	I 28	O 49
H 43	V 34	E 59	J 56	D 63	L 50	M 3	T 24
S 8	R 19	A 64	E 53	F 60	D 25	R 38	N 27
E 35	W 42	B 21	U 6	A 37	I 40	R 23	C 4
O 20	I 7	M 36	N 41	E 22	R 5	E 26	T 39

49 D. This is the only patch that works for all the lines.

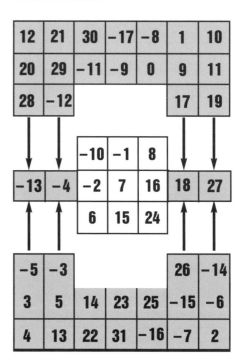

50   7. There are 7 areas of intersection at this position.

51   Lira

I	L	L	I	N	O	I	S
M	I	C	H	I	G	A	N
A	R	K	A	N	S	A	S
M	A	R	Y	L	A	N	D

52   77 square units.

53   25. Star = 9, Whorl = 5, Square = 3

54   Copenhagen.

55   Bogart, Heston, Marvin and Monroe can be found by pairing alternate segments.

56

22	21	13	5	46	38	30
31	23	15	14	6	47	39
40	32	24	16	8	7	48
49	41	33	25	17	9	1
2	43	42	34	26	18	10
11	3	44	36	35	27	19
20	12	4	45	37	29	28

57   34. Write the alphabet in a 3-row grid with the following values: A, J, S = 1; B, K, T = 2; C, L, U = 3; D, M, V = 4; E, N, W = 5; F, O, X = 6; G, P, Y = 7; H, Q, Z = 8; I, R = 9. Thus, Raphael = 9 + 1 + 7 + 8 + 1 + 5 + 3 = 34.

58   2. C = A – B, with the result reversed. 496324 – 235768 = 260556.

59   3. The alphabetical position of the first letter gives the amount.

60   248. Long lines = 2, short lines = 1. Add the values on the right to arrive at the answer.

61   Each value is the sum of Roman numerals in the person's name: Brenda had 500, Axel had 60, Norman had 1000 and Charlie had 151.

62   3. Add the spots and take the middle line from the top line.

63   7. Take the middle number from the top left number. Multiply that by 2 to \ get the top right number. Add 5 to the top right number to get the bottom number.

64   Finishing order is 12, 3, 11, 21, 7 and 8 last.

65   4. Start from the top left of the spiral and work in, successively subtracting and adding: 9 – 7 = 2, 2 + 5 = 7, etc.

66   11954.
(45911 – 11954 = 33957)

67
i)   Odin
ii)   Hermes
iii) Osiris
iv)   Poseidon
v)   Athena
vi)   Cupid

68 Malachi
Genesis
Numbers
Ezekiel
The last letter of two
of the four names is
the same.

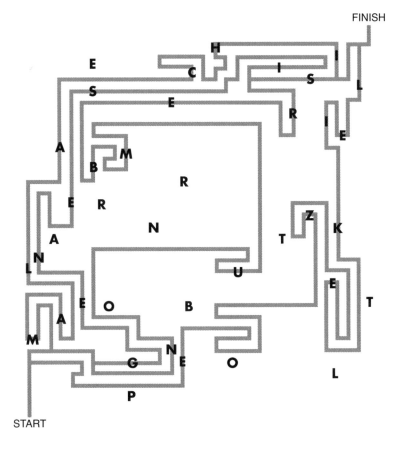

69 Holly Hunter, Sally Field, Daryl
Hannah, Meg Ryan, Demi Moore,
Winona Ryder, Jane Fonda, Bette
Davis.

70 D. The least number of faces touching
each other gives the greatest perimeter.

71 D. The paper would reach
3,355.4432 m, which is as high as a
mountain.

72 McEnroe. The first letter of the first
word gives the first letter of Jean. The
second letter of the second word gives
the second letter of Jean and so on.

73 Brooklyn because it is a city, the others
are states (Florida, Delaware and
Arizona).

74 5 (4 big and 1 little).

75 1003. The Roman numerals in each
name are added together.

76 10.
Snowflake = 5
Candle = 3
Sun = 2

77 Virginia and Delaware.

78 Monarch. The first letters placed
together give the name of Adam.

79

Mr Evans	Mrs Graves	Mrs Davis	Mr Adams
Mrs Harris	Mrs Bates	Mr Francis	Mr Conners

80   Charlie leaves at the 1st floor.
Barbie leaves at the 2nd floor.
Debbie leaves at the 3rd floor.
Angie leaves at the 4th floor.
Frankie leaves at the 5th floor.
Eddie leaves at the 6th floor.

81   P

P	A	R	I	S
I	S	P	A	R
A	R	I	S	P
S	P	A	R	I
R	I	S	P	A

82   D. The the binary numbers start at the top and work left to right, line by line.

1	1	0	1	1	1	0	0	1	0	1
1	1	0	1	1	1	1	0	0	0	1
0	0	1	1	0	1	0	1	0	1	1
1	1	0	0	1	1	0	1	1	1	1
0	1	1	1	1	0	0	0	0	0	1
0	0	0	1	1	0	0	1	0	1	0
0	1	1	1	0	1	0	0	1	0	1
0	1	1	0	1	1	0	1	0	1	1
1	1	1	0	0	0	1	1	0	0	1

83   There are 5 cards missing, leaving 47 in the deck.

84   Daniel, Exodus, Isaiah and Joshua can be found by pairing alternate segments.

85   1. A + B = KL, C + D = MN, and so on.

86   A. The letters outside are consonants of famous tennis players. They are: (top) Borg and Graf, (bottom) Agassi and Cash. The letters inside the triangles are the initials of their nationality. They are Swedish, German, American and Australian respectively.

87   Carlos is oldest; Maccio is youngest. (From oldest to youngest: Carlos, Juan, Za-za, Fifi, Jorjio, Maccio.)

88   21 times.

89   42. The bottom number goes next to the top one to make a two-digit number; the left and right do the same. Then subtract the second number from the first. 96 – 54 = 42.

90   30 x 15 units (the pool's area becomes 18 x 25 units, or 450 square units).

91

6	2	9	3	7
3	7	6	2	9
2	9	3	7	6
7	6	2	9	3
9	3	7	6	2

92 38 seconds after 8.43.

93 J. The vowels have been omitted from the surnames and the initial of the first name is in the middle of the box: Tom Cruise, Johnny Depp, Gary Cooper and John Wayne.

94 6. The right weight is nine units across to balance the left three units across. 6 x 9 (54) balances 18 x 3 (54).

95 19. The top pair of numbers are multipled together and added to the result of multiplying the bottom pair of numbers together. (2 x 8) + (3 x 1).

96 Five men. Each man digs 1 hole in 5 hours, and thus 20 holes in 100 hours.

97 1st and 5th – their final position is based on the number of vowels in their names.

98 12, 19, 26, 3, 10. The bottom line of a Magic Square, in which all rows, columns, and long diagonals equal 70.

99 The scientists are: Celsius, Einstein, Bell, Newton.

100 O. The middle letter of each name is in the middle of the box. Fonda, Hanks, Wayne and Stone.

101 200 Credits. 9 x 25 – (4 x 6.25) = 200.

102 Mel Gibson.

103 88. 88 + 880 + (4 x 8) = 1000.

104 Lamborghini.

105 9 minutes and 9 seconds after 1.

106 8. Each vowel is given a value of one and each consonant is give a value of two. These are added together in each name to give the amount.

PUZZLE CARD ANSWERS

1 INDUCE because all the others have two pronunciations.

2 PETER and PAUL.

3 List them in the following order and you get a magic square which reads the same down as it does across.

LANE
AREA
NEAR
EARS

4 The letters represent numbers based on their position in the alphabet (ie, A = 1, B = 2, etc). The letter square represents a simple subtraction. The final letter is therefore E (5) minus D (4) = A (1).

5 9 cm (all along the four bottom edges, up one vertical edge, then along all the top edges).

6 Noiseless lionesses.

7 18 (consonants are worth 2, vowels 1).

8 Less (the first figure is 3, the second is 16.333.

9 Crocus, all the others are used as girls' names.

10 BARE BEAR.

11 CAR.

12 NIGHT.

13 UP. The others all make a new word if the last letter is repeated.

14 BIRD.

15 70.

16 CARTHORSE

17 AFRICA LION.

18 In FACETIOUS the vowels appear in alphabetical order, in the other words they are in reverse order.

19 Canon / Cannon.

20 DAMNED DEMAND.

21 NOISELESS. All the others are combinations of three three-letter words.

22 I (second letters of the words ONE, TWO, THREE, FOUR, FIVE).

23 D. They are the initial letters of the first five books of the Bible (Genesis, Exodus, Leviticus, Numbers, Deuteronomy).

24 W, E and Y. The sequence is the letters on the top line of a Qwerty keyboard.

25 O. The initial letters of TEN, NINE, EIGHT, SEVEN, etc.

26 ROOK and FELL form an anagram of FOLKLORE.

27   36. The numbers are the squares of 1, 2, 3, 4, 5, 6

28   84. All the others are divisible by 3.

29   In alphabetical order K is the next letter composed entirely of straight lines.

30   300 metres.

31   WILL. (Goodwill and Willpower).

32   DITCH. All the others can be rearranged to make other words.

33   CREATE. All the others conrtain animal names (Ape, Cow, Cat, Pig).

34   REPEAT. All the others contain the names of months.

35   As many times as you like. But the answer will always be the same!

36   Only one, after that the bag is no longer empty.

37   TIRADE.

38   12. They are all numbers with a T in the word.

39   FOUR (it has OUR in it).

40   TENCH (TEN + CH = a fish).

41   4.5lb.

42   Four.

43   1 in 9.

44   No, it's a little bit less. Because a full chamber weighs more than an empty one it is slightly less likely to reach the firing position at the top of the chamber.

45   21 (it is a Fibonacci series).

46   22. Each group must add up to 100.

47   More.

48   All of them except February.

49   31 (Add 1, then 2, then 3, etc).

50   REPLICA (ECLAIR, PLAICE, PARCEL, CARPEL).

Enigma Variations

Edward Elgar

OPUS 36

Order No: NOV 100042R

NOVELLO PUBLISHING LIMITED